Songbirds

The Big Match

Story by Julia Donaldson
Pictures by Chris Mould
Series editor Clare Kirtley

Tips for reading The Big Match together

This book practises these letter patterns:

ng ck x qu

Ask your child to point to these letter patterns and say the sounds (e.g. *x* as in *fox*, not the letter name *ex*). Look out for these letter patterns in the story.

Your child might find these words tricky:

ball begun come here match the

These words are common, but your child may not have learned how to sound them out yet. Say the words for your child if they do not know them.

Before you begin, ask your child to read the title by sounding out and blending as much as possible. Look at the picture together. What do you think this story is about?

Remind your child to read unfamiliar words by saying the individual sounds separately and then blending them together quickly to read the word. When you have finished reading, look through the story again and:

- Talk about why Max Fox got sent off. Ask your child, *How do you think the ducks felt at the end of the story?*

- Find the words which end with the letter pattern *ck* (*duck, quack, kick, Rick*). Say the sound that these two letters make at the end of words. Can you find some words that end with the letter pattern *x*? (*six, fox, Max*).

Here come the fans.

Here come the six ducks.

Here come the six foxes.

The duck fans quack.

The fox fans sing.

The ref rings a bell. The match has begun!

The foxes and ducks kick the ball.

11

Rick Duck gets the ball in.

Max Fox gets the ball in.

The ducks get the ball.

Max Fox kicks Rick Duck!

The duck fans quack.

The ref rings his bell.

Rick Duck gets the ball in!

The duck fans quack and sing.

The ducks win the match.

Songbirds

The Shopping List

Story by Julia Donaldson

Pictures by Anni Axworthy

Series editor Clare Kirtley

OXFORD
UNIVERSITY PRESS

21

Tips for reading The Shopping List together

This book practises blending groups of consonants at the end of words. Look out for these in the story:

went ba**nk** he**ld** li**st** li**ft** go**lf** la**mp** mi**lk**

Your child might find these words tricky:

ball home I like the they to

These words are common, but your child may not have learned how to sound them out yet. Say the words for your child if they do not know them.

Before you begin, ask your child to read the title by sounding out and blending as much as possible. Look at the picture together. What do you think this story is about?

Remind your child to read unfamiliar words by saying the individual sounds separately and then blending them together quickly to read the word. When you have finished reading, look through the story again and:

- Talk about why Yasmin and Dad ended up with the wrong shopping. Ask your child, *What do you think they should do now?*

- Encourage your child to find two words in the story that rhyme (*vest, best; got, lot; back, unpack*). Notice that only the first letter is different. Can you think of any other words that rhyme with *best*? (*nest, test, west*)

Yasmin and Dad went to the bank.

Next, they went shopping.

Yasmin held the shopping list.

belt
golf ball
lamp

Yasmin and Dad went to a big shop.
They got in the lift.

A man got in with them.

30

Yasmin and Dad got back in the lift.

The man got in with them.

Yasmin and Dad went back home.

35

37

Songbirds

Gran is Cross

Story by Julia Donaldson
Pictures by Ross Collins
Series editor Clare Kirtley

OXFORD
UNIVERSITY PRESS

39

Tips for reading Gran is Cross together

This book practises blending groups of consonants at the beginning of words. Look out for these in the story:

twins **Gr**an **fl**ick **br**ings **pr**am **fr**og
steps **bl**ack **Sp**ot **sn**ack **dr**ink **cl**oth
cross **gl**ad **sm**ash

Your child might find these words tricky:

are day go hello home
of the her to

These words are common, but your child may not have learned how to sound them out yet. Say the words for your child if they do not know them.

Before you begin, ask your child to read the title by sounding out and blending as much as possible. Look at the picture together. What do you think this story is about?

Remind your child to read unfamiliar words by saying the individual sounds separately and then blending them together quickly to read the word. When you have finished reading, look through the story again and:

- Talk about how the characters are feeling by the end of the story. Ask your child, *Why do you think Gran was cross?*

- Encourage your child to find words in the story that start with the letters *fr* (*frog, Fred*). Try to write the words. Say all of the sounds in the word separately then write the letter that makes each sound.

The twins go to visit Gran.

Flick brings a pram. Fred brings his frog.

Gran is on the steps.

Gran has a black cat.

Gran gets the twins a snack.

Flick spills her drink on the cloth. Gran is cross.

Fred drops his sandwich in the pram. Gran is cross.

But Spot the cat is glad.

The frog jumps in the jam.
Fred grabs him.

Smash!
Gran is cross.

The frog jumps and jumps.
Spot runs and runs.

The frog jumps on the clock.
Gran is cross.

At the end of the day the twins
go home.

Gran is glad. The twins are glad.

But Spot is sad.

The Trunk and the Skunk

Story by Julia Donaldson
Pictures by Woody
Series editor Clare Kirtley

OXFORD
UNIVERSITY PRESS

Tips for reading The Trunk and the Skunk together

This book practises blending groups of consonants at the beginning and/or end of words. Look out for these in the story:

stamp tu**sks** **tr**unk lift **dr**ink
slosh **sm**ell **sn**iff **sk**unk

Your child might find these words tricky:

bananas good have I my
no of oh the

These words are common, but your child may not have learned how to sound them out yet. Say the words for your child if they do not know them.

Before you begin, ask your child to read the title by sounding out and blending as much as possible. Look at the picture together. What do you think this story is about?

Remind your child to read unfamiliar words by saying the individual sounds separately and then blending them together quickly to read the word. When you have finished reading, look through the story again and:

- Talk about what a mammoth can do with its trunk. Ask your child, *What would you do if you had a trunk?*

- Encourage your child to find two words on page 60 of the story that rhyme (*stamp* and *tramp*). Can they think of other words that rhyme with *stamp? (lamp, damp, camp)*

I am a mammoth.

I have big, thick legs. I can stamp on things.

Stamp, tramp, crash!

I have long tusks. I can
dig with them.

And I have a long trunk.

I can do lots of things with my trunk.

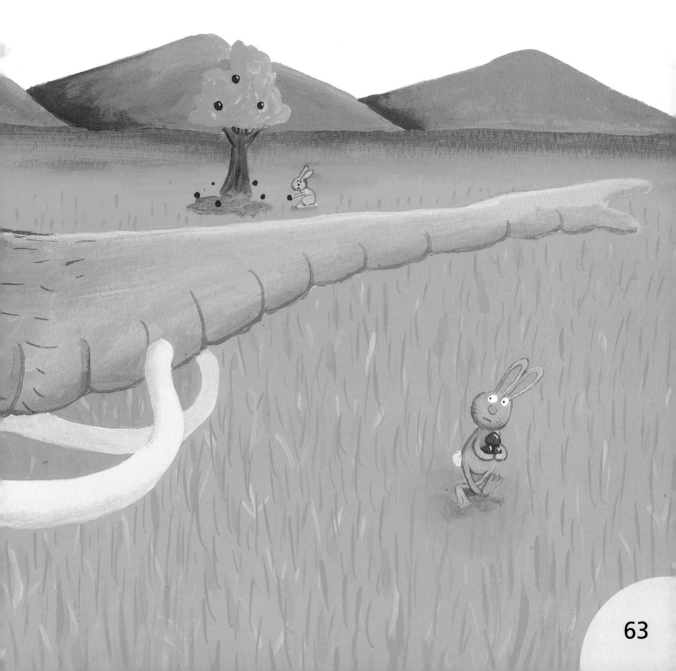

I can pick things up.

I can lift things.

I can drink.

I can slosh my mum and dad!

Stop that!

And I can smell things with my trunk.

I can smell *good* things...
Sniff, sniff! Bananas!

And I can smell *bad* things...
Sniff, sniff! A skunk!

This skunk stinks! I will slosh him!

Slosh! That will get rid of the smell.

Sniff, sniff...

Oh no! The skunk still smells
of skunk.

Songbirds

The Scrap Rocket

Story by Julia Donaldson
Pictures by Jonathan Allen
Series editor Clare Kirtley

OXFORD
UNIVERSITY PRESS

Tips for reading The Scrap Rocket together

This book practises blending groups of consonants at the beginning and/or end of words. Look out for these in the story:

**colle*ct*s *scr*ap a*nd* *pl*a*nk* pu*mp*
*spr*ing *str*ap *cl*i*nk* *tw*i*st* *thr*ill
*spl*ash**

Your child might find this word tricky:

submarine

Explain that we can read longer words by breaking them up into bits. Say the word for your child if they do not know it and explain what it means.

Before you begin, ask your child to read the title by sounding out and blending as much as possible. Look at the picture together. What do you think this story is about?

Remind your child to read unfamiliar words by saying the individual sounds separately and then blending them together quickly to read the word. When you have finished reading, look through the story again and:

- Talk about what Ron Rabbit collected and why. Ask your child, *What would you like to make out of scrap things?*

- Encourage your child to find two words on pages 82 and 83 of the story which rhyme (*spring, string*). Which letters create the rhyme? Can you think of other words that rhyme with *spring*? (*sing, bring, sting, swing, thing, wing, king, ring*)

Ron Rabbit is collecting things.

Ron collects a tin,

a tap,

Ron Rabbit is collecting things.

Ron collects a tin,

a tap,

a pump.

Next, Ron collects a spring,

a strap and

lots of string.

84

It's a rocket!

Lift-off!

But then...

Splash!

It's not a rocket.

It's a submarine!

Songbirds

Splash and Squelch

Story by Julia Donaldson
Pictures by Pauline Siewert
Series editor Clare Kirtley

OXFORD
UNIVERSITY PRESS

93

Tips for reading Splash and Squelch together

This book practises blending groups of consonants at the beginning and/or end of words. Look out for these in the story:

swing **sp**in **spl**ish **squ**elch **st**amp
twigs **st**ump **fr**ogs **spr**ing **fl**op

Your child might find this word tricky:

home   like   to   we

These words are common, but your child may not have learned how to sound them out yet. Say the words for your child if they do not know them.

Before you begin, ask your child to read the title by sounding out and blending as much as possible. Look at the picture together. What do you think this story is about?

Remind your child to read unfamiliar words by saying the individual sounds separately and then blending them together quickly to read the word. When you have finished reading, look through the story again and:

- Talk about why the children had to 'flop' at the end. Ask your child, *Which activities from the story would you like to do?*

- Encourage your child to find words which begin with *spl* (*splish, splash, splosh*). Look closely at each word. What is different about these words (the vowel)? Try to write the words. Say all of the sounds in the word separately then write the letter that makes each sound.

We like to swing.

We like to whizz and spin.

We like to yell in tunnels.

We like to splish, splash and splosh.

We like to run in the sun and dig in the sand.

We like to squelch in the mud and stamp on the twigs.

We like to jump off a log and hit a stump with a stick.

105

We like to hop like frogs

and spring like squirrels.

And when we get home…

we like to flop.

Practise Your Phonics With
Julia Donaldson's
Songbirds

By the Author of The Gruffalo

Look out for the other titles in the series ...

Top Cat and Other Stories
978-0-19-279296-9

The Odd Pet and Other Stories
978-0-19-279297-6

The Ox and the Yak and Other Stories
978-0-19-279298-3

Scrap Rocket and Other Stories
978-0-19-279299-0

Where is the Snail? and Other Stories
978-0-19-279300-3

Tadpoles and Other Stories
978-0-19-279301-0

My Cat and Other Stories
978-0-19-279302-7

Leroy and Other Stories
978-0-19-279303-4

Where Were You Bert? and Other Stories
978-0-19-279304-1